Six Sheep Sip Thick Shakes

The Sheep Shack
Thick Shakes!
Just 3 cents each!

Six Sheep Sip Thick Shakes

And Other Tricky
~~TWONGUE TISTERS~~
TONGUE TWISTERS

Brian P. Cleary

Illustrations by
Steve Mack

SCHOLASTIC INC.
New York Toronto London Auckland
Sydney Mexico City New Delhi Hong Kong

Nan's knapsack straps sat on the striped steps.

The water in Flo's Inn flows in frozen.

The ghostly moans
were mostly groans.

See the Greek geeks
as they shoot
three free throws.

While the cat naps on the mat,
the gnats knit caps.

Miss Tish made a quick list of those she'd kissed quickest.

Sasha shifted as she sifted
through the thistle
for her sister's whistle.

Channel 1: All Movies, All the Time! ($5 per show)

Channel 2: Amazing Sports! ($10 per game)

Channel 3: Bunny News Network (fee free!!)

BUNNY
NEWS
NETWORK

BNN

The TV was fee-free for channel 3.

On Christmas Eve, three thieves see Steve's skis.

To: Steve

Sammy stammered as he told the
stray in the sleigh to stay.

Mrs. Brack's brisket
in the black basket
is sold by the bunches
for breakfast
and brunches.

The people with the purple paper pranced in their pants by the simple steeple.

She sneezed
in her sleeve
as they seized
Mrs. Sleed.

Few knew that Mr. Froo flew in the fleshy, freshly fried fish from Florida.

Brady and Blake broke blackened bread with Blake's brother, Blair.

Patty Packer placed a pint of pricey plum pudding on the platform at the produce plaza.

Fred frowned and fled frantically when he found the flounder in his bed.

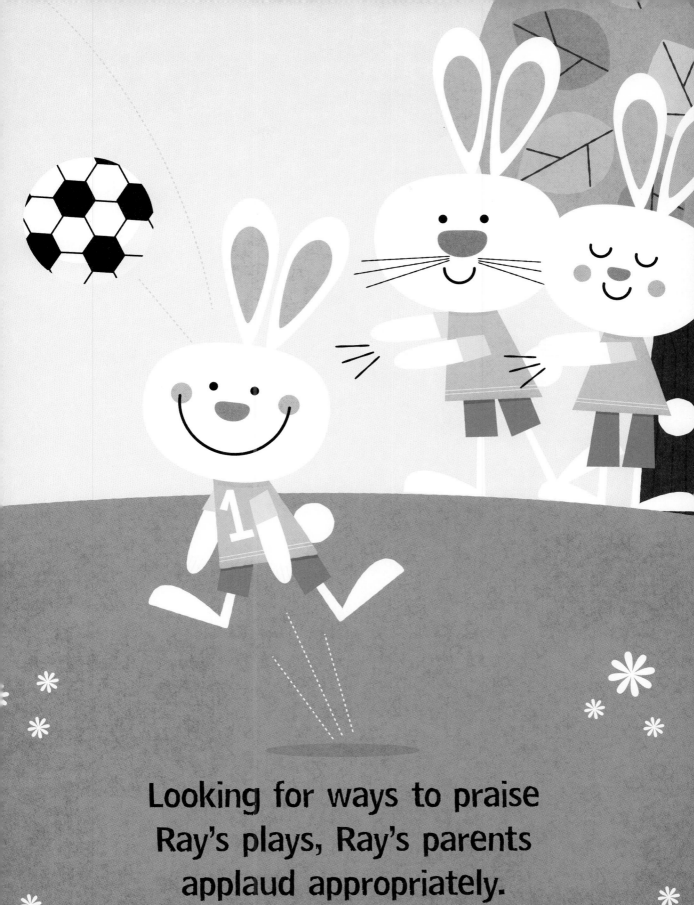

Looking for ways to praise
Ray's plays, Ray's parents
applaud appropriately.

Tim and his thin twin sister, Trish,
twice tricked their thick sitter.

Having purchased a new plow, my pa plowed proudly.

She let the sheik sleep
on the sleek sheet.

As a favor,
my favorite flavor
was placed on my plate.

Six sick sheep on the steep ship sip thick, cheap shakes in the ship's chic sheep shack.

Two-ton trains transporting twelve three-toed turtles twist trickily on the twin train tracks.

Make Your Own Tongue Twisters

You can make tongue twisters of your own! To find out how, first you'll need to learn how tongue twisters work—and just why they are so difficult to say out loud.

Tongue twisters are sentences or phrases that combine similar sounds in repetition. Often the more words there are in a tongue twister, the harder it is to pronounce each of the words the first time through. Sometimes, the similar sounds are at the beginning of the words, as in:

Sammy stammered as he told the stray in the sleigh to stay.

Note that the use of words beginning with s, st, str, and sl makes your tongue do all sorts of gymnastics to get the sentence right!

Other times, the "twist" is at the back end of the words, like it is here:

While the cat naps on the mat, the gnats knit caps.

The ending letters of t, ps, and ts are what cause all the commotion.

Certain letter combinations can be particularly difficult to pronounce. Take these, for example:

gr/gl/g
fr/fl/f
th/s/st/str
br/bl/b
pr/pl/p
sh/sl/s
sw/sl/st
tw/tr/t

The dictionary will give you bunches of words that start with these tongue-twister-friendly combinations. Take a look—and then get to work writing your own tongue twisters. Your own imagination is your only limitation!

To my friends at Price Laboratory School
—b.p.c.

For Alex and Ava, my two little art directors
—s.m.

ISBN 978-0-545-45834-4

Text copyright © 2011 by Brian P. Cleary.
Illustrations copyright © 2011 by Steve Mack.
All rights reserved. Published by Scholastic Inc., 557 Broadway, New York, NY 10012, by arrangement with Millbrook Press, a division of Lerner Publishing Group, Inc. SCHOLASTIC and associated logos are trademarks and/or registered trademarks of Scholastic Inc.

12 11 10 9 8 7 6 5 4 3 2 1   12 13 14 15 16 17/0

                                              08

Printed in the U.S.A.

First Scholastic printing, March 2012